The Bach Flower Gardener

By the same author

Bach Flower Remedies for Men
The Bach Remedies Workbook

STEFAN BALL

The Bach Flower Gardener

Index compiled
by Lyn Greenwood

SAFFRON WALDEN
THE C.W. DANIEL COMPANY LIMITED

First published in Great Britain in 1999
by The C.W. Daniel Company Limited
1 Church Path, Saffron Walden,
Essex, CB10 1JP, United Kingdom

ISBN 0 85207 329 1

Two climbing roses at
Book Production Consultants, 25–27 High Street,
Chesterton, Cambridge, CB4 1ND orchardstrated the
production. The typesetting was accomplished by
Cambridge Photosetting Services, Cambridge.
Printed & bound by Biddles, Guildford

Contents

For Chris

And 'tis my faith that every flower
Enjoys the air it breathes.

WILLIAM WORDSWORTH,
Lines Written in Early Spring

Introduction

About this book

People all over the world know of the system of 38 flower remedies discovered by Dr Bach. It is a system so gentle that remedies can be given even to new-born children with perfect safety. It does not react with other medicines, so that therapists who specialise in other treatments often use it as a complement to their main techniques. Its focus on the emotions makes it a natural partner to the more physically-oriented approaches of most orthodox and non-orthodox medical traditions. And above all it is effective – which is why the use of this system has spread via personal recommendation and word of mouth from one small corner of Oxfordshire to more than 66 countries around the world.

Many people have used the 38 remedies – and in particular the so-called 39th remedy, a mixture of five individual Bach Flower Remedies sold under the trade mark 'Rescue Remedy' – to help animals. This has happened almost from the day they were discovered. A case history reprinted in *The Original Writings of Edward Bach* tells how Dr Bach himself gave what is believed to have been Rescue Remedy to a dying white pony, which promptly and unexpectedly recovered.

These uses are common currency. It is somewhat less well known that the remedies can be used just as effectively to help plants. John Ramsell gives some examples in his book *Questions and Answers*: "A plant that has been uprooted accidentally, or transplanted elsewhere, will require Rescue Remedy for shock, and most certainly Walnut to help it adjust to its new habitat." Judy Howard also mentions the topic in her book *Bach Flower Remedies Step by Step*; and both authors give a few hints on the practicalities of selecting remedies for plants. According to the latter, plants "display their outlook through their appearance", using a sort of vegetable body language to give us clues about which remedies they need.

Even earlier than this, scattered examples of this kind of use appeared in the Bach Centre's *Newsletter*, which has been published three times a year since 1950. Nora Weeks and Victor Bullen, who edited the *Newsletter* for many years, took a special interest in the subject, and published an appeal for news from anyone using the remedies in this way so as to collect more information.

Up to now, however, and despite the Centre's interest in it, the use of remedies to help plants has remained something of a marginal activity. Nobody has collected together the nuggets of advice that lie hidden in different places. It seemed to me that there was room for a book dedicated wholly to this use of the remedies: hence the present volume.

My main aim in writing this book has been to encourage experimentation among gardeners. In particular I would like to encourage people to try using the whole system of remedies, and not just the old standby Rescue Remedy. It is perfectly safe to experiment with the others, since the remedies can do no harm whatsoever to plants. And the effort may bring its own rewards.

What I mean by this can be explained in a few words. I believe that the effort of imagination needed to empathise with a living thing so different from ourselves can only increase our own sense of our place in the world. It will itself put us into a clearer and closer relationship with the rest of the living universe. Furthermore, by considering how the remedies might apply to plants we can gain a deeper insight into the remedies themselves. This will stand us in good stead when we go back to using them on ourselves. To these hopes (and to the good of your roses) this book is dedicated.

A word on natural gardening

Implicit in this book, and in everything to do with Dr Bach and his work, is respect for nature and a desire to live a more natural life. The search for harmony in our houses, and above all in our gardens, is a reflection of the search for balance within ourselves.

The subject of organic and wildlife gardening is a vast one, and quite deliberately I have not tried to add more to the many millions of words already written on that subject. If you are already an organic gardener you will not need to be persuaded of the benefits of a more natural approach. If you are not, then I hope that this book will encourage you to follow in Dr Bach's footsteps and look at your garden – whether window-boxed or landscaped – with a renewed sense of wonder and responsibility.

Acknowledgements

The first debt to be acknowledged is of course to Dr Bach, and to all those who have continued his work since his death. Old roses used to smell of heaven until they were improved to the point that they lost their perfume; those who have followed Dr Bach have taken on the extremely difficult task of not improving on perfection.

Information gathered from chance conversations and random books has taken root here, and has branched out in unexpected directions. I owe a huge debt to the many practitioners and other correspondents who responded to appeals for help by allowing me to use samples of their own gardening experiences. These cuttings have been carefully arranged in part three, along with some choice blooms from old *Newsletters*, all clearly labelled, and I acknowledge these with thanks.

My wife Chris pruned and clipped around the borders of this book (and took care of our real garden) and our children Alexandra, Madeleine and Ethan gave it room to grow (as I hope we have done for them).

Finally, and in addition, and in no particular order, the onerous task of digging over fresh earth and laying out paths was eased by BBC Radio 3, Microsoft Word 95, the members of various internet newsgroups, a number of German brewers and European, South African and South American vineyards, Ralph Vaughan Williams, and lashings of Perrier water with a dash of lemon.

PART 1:

Dr Bach's Work

Healing with the clean, pure, beautiful agents of nature is surely the one method of all which appeals to most of us, and deep down in our inner self surely there is something about it that rings true indeed, something which tells us: this is nature's way, and is right.

EDWARD BACH

Dr Bach and his discoveries

Dr Edward Bach (pronounced 'Batch' since his university days) was a respected bacteriologist, pathologist and Harley Street physician. He was born in 1886 and qualified as a doctor in 1912. In 1930 he left London and an income of some £5,000 a year in order to walk the length of England and Wales, finding and preparing a total of 38 remedies before announcing in 1935 that his work was complete. A year later, in 1936, he died.

These are the bald facts. They conceal an incredible story of personal courage and commitment.

Bach was repeatedly turned down for military service in the First World War on the grounds of ill health, yet he took charge of 400 wartime hospital beds at University College Hospital in London, spending every spare moment working at his research into bowel disease. In 1917 he suffered a severe haemorrhage, collapsed, and was operated on for cancer. When he recovered consciousness he was told he had only three months to live. As soon as he could get out of bed he went back to his research work, determined to bring it to a conclusion if he could. His window at the hospital was known as "the light that never goes out" because of the long hours he kept.

Months went by; his health unexpectedly recovered. It seemed that the less thought he gave to his illness the stronger he became. The realisation that this was so confirmed for him a belief he had held ever since his student days: the state of mind of a sick person was pivotal to successful recovery. He had got better because he had a purpose in life, and was doing work that he believed in.

This work was aimed at the treatment of intestinal toxaemia, and had already gained Bach an excellent reputation in the medical world. He isolated bacilli from the intestines of patients suffering from certain chronic diseases, and when he prepared these bacilli as vaccines he was able to treat these hitherto incurable conditions.

In 1919 Dr Bach started work in a new post as pathologist and bacteriologist at the London Homoeopathic Hospital. Here for the first time he encountered homoeopathy and in particular its seminal text, Samuel Hahnemann's *Organon*. He was singularly impressed by the fact that Hahnemann had seen a connection between intestinal toxaemia and chronic disease over a century before. His own modern, orthodox methods had in effect confirmed the work of this great pioneer. Hahnemann wrote of the need to treat the whole person rather than the symptoms of disease alone, and stressed the importance of the mental state of the person being treated; as he read this, perhaps Dr Bach's mind went back to his own recent brush with death.

It was not long before Dr Bach started to prepare his bacterial vaccines homoeopathically, as nosodes, or oral vaccines. There were seven vaccines, one for each group of bacteria he isolated, and as part of his new homoeopathic approach, Bach looked at the 'mentals' of each nosode – in other words, at the mental and emotional states of the people being treated with that particular medicine.

It became apparent that bacteria of a particular group were associated with a particular group of personality types and particular mental states. Up to now Bach had selected nosodes for people by the orthodox method of preparing samples by plating, and examining the resulting cultures. Excited by the possibility of a less intrusive method he tried to predict which nosodes his patients would need based purely on their personality type. The results were impressive. He lost no time in publishing details of his work, hoping in this way to spread knowledge of his discoveries to anyone who might benefit from them.

The flower remedies grew out of this initial work with the nosodes. The seeds were sown by Dr Bach's dislike of using bacteria – the products of disease – as a cure for disease. He wanted to find natural, pure equivalents for the seven bacterial nosodes in nature's garden. So he began to experiment with plants that had similar effects to the bacilli, hoping to find the seven plants that would replace the seven nosodes.

At first the results were disappointing; but a breakthrough came in 1928. It began in the unlikely setting of a formal dinner.

Bach was a reluctant guest. To cure his boredom he began examining the faces, gestures and mannerisms of the other guests. He was struck by the similarities between some individuals, and saw that it would be possible to class them together as types, as if they were members of the same emotional family. Comparing these new groups with the seven nosodes, he saw that in fact there was no exact match: there were more than seven personality groupings, and more basic emotions and states of mind.

Insight came to him in a flash. He saw that he would have to go much further than simply replacing the seven nosodes with seven new remedies. The goal was not to treat chronic disease alone; instead it must be to find the individual remedies for each of the basic emotions and personality types that he would identify. If he could do that he would have a system that would strike disease where it had its beginning, in the minds and hearts of individual sufferers.

The early autumn of that year found him in Wales, where he gathered samples of the plants *Impatiens glandulifera* and *Mimulus guttatus*. Back in London he prepared them in the same way he had prepared so many other plants before. On this occasion however the results were better than he dared to hope: there was a clear relationship between the actions of these plants and some of the personality and emotional groups that he had begun to sketch out at the dinner. Patients treated with them reported excellent results.

He added one more remedy to the list – Clematis – and by the end of the following year had given up using any other medicines, while he looked for more remedy plants to prepare. Then, in 1930, as we have seen, he left London to devote himself entirely to the search for new remedies.

Between 1930 and early 1934 Dr Bach divided his time between this search, which occupied the spring and summer of each year and took him to many scattered corners of England and Wales, and winter months spent in Cromer in Norfolk, where he saw patients. He had found, prepared and tested 19 remedies, using a new and remarkably simple method of preparation, by the time he settled in Sotwell, Oxfordshire, in a small rented Victorian cottage called Mount Vernon.

Here Dr Bach spent the last two and a half years of his life. To his delight he found that almost all of the nineteen remedies he had already discovered grew wild in the countryside roundabout; and in a burst of activity the following year he found a further nineteen remedies. The system of flower remedies was complete.

In the period when he was travelling around England and Wales Dr Bach walked almost everywhere. During the discovery of the final nineteen remedies he suffered himself from the negative states of mind for which the remedy was needed, and often these states were accompanied by severe physical illness as well. By the end of

1935 he was very tired, but he did not spare himself.

The many successes of his new remedies brought a queue of patients to the door of Mount Vernon. He turned nobody away. He wrote up the final results of his many researches, and then in Summer 1936 he planned a lecture tour. The first talk was held in the nearby town of Wallingford, on the 24th September 1936, his fiftieth birthday; by the end of October, however, he was very sick. The illness of almost twenty years before and his untiring commitment to his work had taken their toll. Dr Bach had completed his researches; worn out, he died peacefully on November 27th 1936.

Dr Bach's garden

Dr Bach loved nature, and loved the garden at Mount Vernon. This comes across clearly in *The Story of Mount Vernon*, where Judy Howard tells of his activity in the garden when he first moved into the house in 1934:

> Dr Bach was busy and happy for several weeks, digging and weeding and making paths with all the slate and stones he could find lying about. He cleared the borders

and made a small lawn and then planted vegetables and flower seeds. He always talked to his plants and seeds as he put them in the ground, saying "Be happy with us, we will look after you."

Everything he planted flourished and responded quickly and splendidly to his care. He used to say, "A little love in a garden is far better than a cartload of manure", and indeed the garden soon became so full of vegetables that it was impossible to keep up with their growth.

The remedies

Each remedy that Dr Bach found is aimed at a particular mood – so there is one remedy for self-pity, another for jealousy and another for terror and so on. Sometimes single remedies are used; sometimes up to seven remedies are mixed together to make individual treatments.

Some of the remedies are more obviously relevant to plants than others; some at first glance appear not to be relevant at all. We will look more closely at how individual selections for plants can be made in part 2 of this book. For the moment, however, it will be useful to get an overview of the 38 remedies and the basic emotions for which they are used. In alphabetical order they are:

AGRIMONY
Indications: appears content and happy, but there is emotional torment hidden under the surface.
Treatment goal: allow expression and assimilation of hidden torment.

ASPEN
Indications: general, free-floating fear, with no definite named cause.
Treatment goal: lack of fear and anxiety; grounded more in the real world.

BEECH
Indications: unable to tolerate different ways of living.
Treatment goal: increase tolerance.

CENTAURY
Indications: serves the needs of others at the cost of its own needs; unable to set boundaries.
Treatment goal: serve with wisdom and strength.

CERATO
Indications: imitates others and seeks advice due to lack of inner faith in one's chosen path.
Treatment goal: trusts oneself.

CHERRY PLUM
Indications: loss of self-control.
Treatment goal: mastery of self.

CHESTNUT BUD
Indications: continued repetition of the same error.
Treatment goal: ability to learn from experience.

CHICORY
Indications: possessive, selfish love.
Treatment goal: selfless love.

CLEMATIS
Indications: emotions are engaged in vague dreams and not in the present.
Treatment goal: more interest in the present and the real world.

CRAB APPLE
Indications: feelings of contamination and dirtiness; dislike of one's own appearance.
Treatment goal: the cleansing remedy.

ELM
Indications: feelings of being overwhelmed by responsibility.
Treatment goal: restore ability to cope and to take on responsibility.

GENTIAN
Indications: despondency and discouragement after something has gone wrong.
Treatment goal: give encouragement.

GORSE
Indications: pessimistic despair and loss of hope faced with a problem, illness etc. (In some ways, the next stage on from the Gentian state.)
Treatment goal: restore hope and a positive view.

HEATHER
Indications: desperate for company; saps others' vitality; self-obsessed.
Treatment goal: lack of concern with self.

HOLLY

Indications: strong, negative feelings towards others, such as suspicion, hatred and jealousy.
Treatment goal: generosity and love towards others.

HONEYSUCKLE

Indications: emotions stuck in the past; lack of interest in the present and future.
Treatment goal: live in the present.

HORNBEAM

Indications: lack of the energy required to start work.
Treatment goal: the strength to begin.

IMPATIENS

Indications: living in a hurry, no patience with delay or slowness.
Treatment goal: patience.

LARCH

Indications: not enough confidence to try; lack of self-confidence.
Treatment goal: confidence to try, and not to mind failure.

MIMULUS

Indications: fear of something that can be named; timidity.

Treatment goal: quiet courage.

MUSTARD

Indications: gloominess for no known reason.

Treatment goal: lift the clouds and let in the light.

OAK

Indications: slow, methodical and strong; continues even when rest is required.

Treatment goal: support at times of exhaustion; ability to rest when necessary.

OLIVE

Indications: exhaustion after an effort has been made.

Treatment goal: convalescence and recovery of strength.

PINE

Indications: takes on guilt for anything that goes wrong.

Treatment goal: accept responsibility at appropriate times, then move on.

RED CHESTNUT

Indications: fear and anxiety about what will happen to others.

Treatment goal: trust, confidence and courage in the fate of others.

ROCK ROSE

Indications: terror.

Treatment goal: courage and strength of purpose.

ROCK WATER

Indications: desire for perfection leads to self-denial and rigidity of outlook.

Treatment goal: flexibility and the ability to enjoy life's pleasures.

SCLERANTHUS

Indications: indecision between options, lack of certainty.

Treatment goal: decisiveness.

STAR OF BETHLEHEM

Indications: shock, trauma, great loss.

Treatment goal: comfort loss, soothe shock.

SWEET CHESTNUT

Indications: extreme anguish and despair, when there is no way out to be found.

Treatment goal: renewed faith and hope.

VERVAIN

Indications: exuberance, enthusiasm and energy, carried to extremes of perfectionism, fanaticism and tension.

Treatment goal: ability to relax and achieve wisdom and calm.

VINE

Indications: ruthlessness; strength used to dominate and control.

Treatment goal: use strength to lead rather than dominate.

WALNUT

Indications: unsettled during or after a change; tempted away from correct path by outside influences, either past or present.

Treatment goal: give confidence to continue on the correct path.

WATER VIOLET
Indications: remote, self-sufficient, fond of solitude, leading to isolation and the appearance of pride.
Treatment goal: able to take part in the life of the group.

WHITE CHESTNUT
Indications: preoccupied with constant, repetitive worries.
Treatment goal: a calm mind, filled with quiet and peace.

WILD OAT
Indications: no clear purpose in life, leading to frustration, boredom and despondency.
Treatment goal: aid decision on the right path to follow.

WILD ROSE
Indications: drifting, resigned to the way things are; apathy.
Treatment goal: take more interest in life and act with more purpose.

WILLOW

Indications: self-pity, resentment, bitterness; blaming others when things go wrong.

Treatment goal: generosity towards others; optimism.

Rescue Remedy

As was mentioned in the introduction, there is also one ready-mixed treatment, which is sold under the brand name Rescue Remedy. This is an emergency mix of five remedies that is designed to help overcome the emotions associated with crisis situations and stressful events.

The remedies in Rescue Remedy are:
- Star of Bethlehem – shock and trauma
- Impatiens – agitation, impatience
- Clematis – faint, far-away feelings
- Rock Rose – terror
- Cherry Plum – loss of self-control

Rescue Cream

This is designed as a convenient way to apply Rescue Remedy externally. It contains Crab Apple, the cleansing remedy, in addition to the usual five Rescue Remedy ingredients.

Crab Apple is included because the cream is used for the external trauma associated with emotional trauma: blemishes on a person or plant are linked to feelings of dirtiness and self-dislike. The Crab Apple is there as an emotional cleanser.

Can you grow the remedy plants yourself?

The only cultivated plant that we use when we make the remedies is Cerato. This is a native of Tibet, and in Britain only grows in gardens. Dr Bach chose this plant, but in every other case specifically said that cultivated plants should not be used.

Most of the other plants and trees used are native or naturalised, and grow wild in the British countryside. The three exceptions are Vine and Olive, which do not grow wild in Britain and are prepared in southern Europe, and Rock Water, which is the only flower remedy that is not made using flowers. Instead it is water from a healing spring, prepared using Dr Bach's methods.

We use many of the plants that grow in the garden at Mount Vernon, which is a semi-wild garden, where the plants are left to seed and grow wherever they want, and where the minimum of actual gardening is done – we pull out the more rampant weeds that would otherwise take over, but that is pretty much all.

You can grow the remedy plants in your garden as long as you have the right kind of conditions to allow them to grow. But if you want to try your hand at preparing remedies, your garden needs to be as natural and wild as the one at Mount Vernon, and the climatic and soil conditions need to be the same as they are here. Nora Weeks, Dr Bach's assistant and custodian of the work after his death, was very clear on this point shortly before her death in 1978:

> We ask those living abroad not to prepare the essences even if the flowers have the same Latin name, for due to the difference in soil and climate they will not give the same effect.

You also need to be especially careful not to allow hybridisation of the remedy plants, which can easily happen if garden and wild varieties of a plant are growing in the same area. It is also very easy to inadvertently pick the wrong variety, since many of the flowers used have near relations with very few differences – and again using the wrong flower will result in an essence that will not work.

If you are interested in learning more about the remedy plants, the book to read is *Bach Flower Remedies: Illustrations and Preparations*, by Nora Weeks and Victor Bullen. This includes colour pictures of the remedy plants and full details of their Latin names and growing habits. You can order it from the Bach Centre (see address on page 96) or from any good book shop.

PART 2:

Using the Remedies

There is no question that plants have all kinds of sensitivities. They do a lot of responding to their environment. They can do almost anything you can think of. But just because they sit there, anybody walking down the road considers them just a plastic area to look at, as if they're not really alive.

BARBARA MCCLINTOCK

Do plants have emotions?

As we have seen in the preceding chapter, the remedies counteract negative emotions and mental states such as fear, lack of confidence and over-enthusiasm. The first question that arises when one considers using these remedies to help plants is this: how can plants be said to have emotions? How can something that lacks a mind have a mental state?

Before attempting to deal with this question it might be a good idea to get rid of some of the unwanted political baggage that might get in the way of a considered response. The question of whether or not plants have feelings leads to the vexed question of whether plants feel pain. That in turn leads us into political territory which the different sides in the animal rights debate have battled over for many years.

Vested interests in the meat industry have seized on evidence that plants have feelings, and claimed that it shows the basic hypocrisy of vegetarians and animal rights campaigners. The argument goes like this: you say it is wrong to cause suffering to animals by farming and/or eating them; you are however happy to farm and eat plants; this research shows that plants also feel pain; therefore you are a hypocrite.

There are two very simple answers to this argument. The first lies in the fact that everyone has to eat, and that means not just humans but the animals that humans eat. Every piece of pork or lamb in the supermarket has been fed on many times its own weight in seeds, grains, grass and so on. This means that the real choice is not between killing plants or animals, but between killing just plants, or killing animals plus a whole lot more plants. Vegetarians can therefore answer the meat industry argument by pointing out that even if they are still causing some suffering they are causing less total suffering than meat-eaters.

The second answer to the meat industry's hypocrisy argument is to say that unlike animals, many parts of the vegetable kingdom rely on being eaten as part of fulfilling their basic function. The reason that plants produce succulent fruit and edible nuts is that they want animals to eat them. They know that this is an excellent way of depositing a seed some distance away, ready-packaged with some nice fresh manure.

Dr Bach himself went further than this. He believed that the plants we eat were actually provided by nature in order to support other forms of existence, including human beings. This is why when he started looking for remedy plants, he knew he would not find what he wanted among food plants, which were already fulfilling their purpose. The true healing plants would be those whose purpose was still not understood.

Dr Bach's ideas on this subject found corroboration in the 1960s, when an American expert in the use of lie-detecting equipment, called Cleve Backster, found that plants seemed to 'close down' or 'faint' when they felt particularly threatened. The person about to eat a plant could in some sense mesmerise it into a quiet acceptance of this state of affairs. Backster wondered if some plants might in fact enter this state willingly, and in effect be happy to be eaten by an animal and so become part of a different form of existence.

Certainly we ourselves have never felt culpable or guilty about gathering flowers and twigs to make the remedies: we believe that they are here to help us, and that there is – if you like – a state of mutual gratitude involved in making the remedies. We are grateful to the plant for the remedy, and the plant is grateful for having fulfilled its purpose in a higher scheme of things.

The two arguments presented above – the reduction in total suffering, and the fulfilling of the plant's purpose – should be powerful enough by themselves to refute the charge of hypocrisy. Nevertheless, some animal rights campaigners have gone the extra mile and dismissed talk of plant emotions out of hand. No doubt they believe that if they can show that plants do not feel anything then that too refutes the meat industry's argument. Other, professional sceptics also find it hard to accept that there are emotions to be found anywhere outside the animal kingdom. So how can we speak of a plant being 'happy' to be eaten? What evidence is there that plants really do have emotions?

According to the best-selling book *The Secret Life of Plants* by Peter Tompkins and Christopher Bird there is in fact quite a lot of evidence for this belief. Much of it comes from the former Soviet Union. In the 1970s, for example, a Soviet professor called V. N. Pushkin published accounts of research into plants and their reactions to human emotional states. According to him there were grounds for thinking that at a cellular level, plants were carrying out the same basic activities that in us have evolved into human thought. Another Soviet scientist reported tortured plants that responded with wild fear when the torturer approached, and calmed down when a carer came near.

Another study carried out in Russia found that plants could be conditioned in much the same way as Pavlov's famous dogs. A plant given electric shocks whenever a piece of rock was placed next to it eventually learned to associate the two events, and produced the same (seemingly emotional) response when the rock was brought in without an actual shock being given.

Much of this work has been met with frank incredulity by mainstream scientists and thinkers. They argue that emotions are only there as a result of complex structures. Breathing requires lungs, a throat and a nose, and in the same way emotions and consciousness require a central nervous system, made up of nerves and a brain. Since scientists cannot find any evidence of equivalent complex systems in plants, they therefore argue that they are not there, and that plants do not have emotions or any kind of recognisable mental states.

There are of course huge differences between the organisation of plants and animals. We should not however allow ourselves to be so blinded by these differences that we become incapable of seeing equally large similarities.

On a genetic level, there are precious few differences between us and our closest animal relatives, the chimpanzees: 99% of our genes are identical. Indeed, all living organisms – including plants – share the same twenty amino acids, and the same genetic code is used by all to make a variety of substances including riboflavin, thiamine, myosin, actin, and certain vitamins. The similarities between plants and ourselves actually outweigh the obvious differences, as the sociobiologist Edward O. Wilson points out:

> Other species are our kin. This perception is literally true in evolutionary time. All higher eukaryotic organisms, from flowering plants to insects and humanity itself, are thought to have descended from a single ancestral population that lived about 1.8 billion years ago. (*The Biophilia Hypothesis*, 1993)

Over the last hundred years, many people have suggested that it *is* in fact possible to have emotions without a recognisable central nervous system. To paraphrase the Bengali scientist Sir Jagadis Chandra Bose, plants breathe, eat and move without the aid of lungs, gills, stomach or muscles – why then could they not feel without a brain or nerves?

In a series of experiments, Bose showed how plants reacted to stimuli such as touch, poison, heat and electric shocks in ways that exactly corresponded to the way that animal nerves-plus-muscle responded. Furthermore, they grew tired if they were stimulated too much, just like animals, and he was even able to measure reactions to alcohol that were remarkably close to drunkenness…

Many people swear that trying to communicate with plants, either by talking to them, or simply by thinking kindly of them, can improve their growth – and this too can be taken as evidence of some sort of mental function in plants. Luther Burbank, a pioneer horticulturalist with a genius for breeding new varieties of vegetables, fruits and flowers, was one example. He was known to talk to his plants when he wanted to encourage them in some new direction. Another was the famous African-American botanist George Washington Carver, who revolutionised agriculture with his work on peanuts and other crops. He used to sing to his plants.

No less a figure than Charles Darwin could write of a young plant's growing radicle, its main root, that its tip "acts like the brain of one of the lower animals, … receiving impressions from the sense organs, and directing the several movements." To an unbiased eye this looks remarkably like the description of a kind of nervous system. And a professor at Texas State University in the 1940s, E. J. Lund, has demonstrated the presence of electric impulses in plants which, in the eyes of some, could take the place of the physical nervous system of animals.

Nobody can pretend that views like this are without their critics, and for every person who supports similar readings of plant life there are hundreds who deny their validity. The thesis that plants *do* have emotions is not proven, then, and as with the remedies themselves, it will stand or fall according to how successful it ends up being in the real world.

How the remedies work

In the case of the remedies, success in the real world has demonstrated their effectiveness, despite the fact that they are prepared in such a way that no physical traces of the plants used are left in the bottles that you buy in the shop. The active ingredient is not a physical substance, but the life force of the plant itself. This has been described as an energy, and as a vibration, but the best description is still the one that Dr Bach gave when he likened this captured life force to beautiful music that uplifts the spirit, and raises the life force of the person, animal or plant taking it to a higher level.

Dr Bach's music analogy may go a long way to explaining why the remedies can be as effective for plants as they are for animals and people. In the 1950s and 60s a botanist in Madras, India, Dr T. C. Singh, performed a series of experiments that showed how plant activity and growth was stimulated by the playing of traditional Indian music. Similar experiments have been carried out around the world, by botanists, florists, farmers and musicians, resulting in increased yields of wheat and turnip crops and a lot of puzzled theorising.

Other experiments have tried to measure the different responses plants show to different types of music: Dorothy Retallack, in a famous series of experiments, found that plants grew towards speakers playing harmonious classical Western and Indian music, while heavy percussive rock music caused them to grow poorly, and as far away from the speakers as they could get.

More recent research into the positive effects of J. S. Bach's music on the performance of people is an interesting parallel and support to the work done on plants. And there are of course millions of stories of both people and plants responding to the remedies. Perhaps the 'music' discovered by Dr Bach is closer to J. S. Bach than it is to Black Sabbath...

Selecting remedies for plants

If we accept that the beautiful music of the remedies can raise the vibrations of plants as well as of people, there is still a major difficulty to overcome before we can use them in this way. It is not enough to believe that plants have feelings – we now need a way of understanding what those feelings actually are.

Most people do not really try to select remedies for plants: they give Rescue Remedy instead. Plants get Rescue Remedy far more than they get any other remedy simply because it can be applied without there being any need to isolate the specific emotions being felt by them. Instead the rule-of-thumb reasoning, when faced with a sick or struggling plant, is this: something is wrong so it must be under stress; Rescue Remedy will help it cope.

As far as it goes there is nothing wrong with this reasoning, and there are many case studies that show how successful it can be – as part 3 of this book will show. But we should be able to go much further, and actually come up with personalised mixes for groups of plants, and for individual plants. How then do we go about this? We can see how a personal mix of remedies can be arrived at for a person, or for an animal – especially one we know well – but how can this be achieved for a plant?

It has been said of the Nobel prize-winning biologist Barbara McClintock that she was so aware of the plants she worked with that she was able to write an individual biography for each one. This might seem like a mystical ability that only very special people could have; but in fact it boils down to a simple mix of observation and empathy. We may not have the genius of McClintock, but application of these same skills can allow all of us to see differences not just in the way groups of plants react, but also between any two individual plants. We too can begin to write biographies of our plants; or to try to tell the story from the plant's point of view, to make it read like an autobiography.

Human beings have been doing this ever since we first learned to use language. We have put ourselves in the place of the animals and plants that we eat, in order to understand them and so predict their behaviour. "If I were an antelope, when would I visit the waterhole? – If I were a peach, what time of year would I want to ripen?"

This is anthropomorphism, an assumed dialogue with sentient nature, which in the scientific world – and despite the glittering careers of mavericks like McClintock – is often condemned as useless and sure to lead us astray. This condemnation ignores the fact that it has made us what we are today and has given us our pre-eminent position among living creatures. Viewing the rest of nature as imbued with meaning allows us to learn from what actually happens, and apply that learning in new contexts: an angry sea is a dangerous sea, so best to stay in port; but if you have to go out, make your boat with planks of oak. With the remedies, we can use this same ability of thinking ourselves into other creatures to try to give something back to the plants and animals.

So if a seedling is being re-potted, Walnut is one obvious remedy to help adjust to the change, perhaps with Star of Bethlehem for the shock of being dug out and replanted – that is a plausible way of describing how the plant may feel, and if it turns out to be accurate, the remedies will work. In the same way we can suggest that Crab Apple – the remedy for feelings of contamination and dislike of one's own appearance – may be helpful for plants that have been infested with parasites or have been damaged. A plant that has lost its vigour because it has been kept too close to a radiator could be given Olive to restore its dissipated energy; on the other hand, one that fails to thrive despite every apparent advantage might benefit instead from Hornbeam, or from Centaury or Willow or Gentian.

Naturally, this process involves guesswork. This is not a vast problem, however, since the remedies will not do any harm if we select the wrong ones. This means that we can try out different combinations until we hit on the right one, and have the comfort of knowing that at the very least we will not be making the problem worse.

Type remedies for plants

When we select remedies for people or for animals, we try to do a bit more than select for the passing moods and emotions alone. We also spend time thinking about the basic personality of the creature we are treating, so as to identify where possible the *type remedy* that applies to its own individual character. The type remedy indicates how that particular creature will tend to react when things go wrong. It is usually the remedy that the individual concerned will need to use most often.

Do plants have type remedies in the same way? Certainly, if we are going to write the biography of a plant we need to look for it, if it is there, because the type remedy is the basic character sketch. Without it the biography will not take wing. It will be a simple chronicle – a succession of events with no sense of motive or personality.

We have already seen that when selecting for plants the ideal is to 'get inside the plant's head' (so to speak) so as to get a feel for how it might respond. Once you have given this kind of attention to a plant a few times you may well begin to see a pattern developing, and that may indicate the type remedy. You can also note the way the plant tends to react when things are against it, and this too can be a clue.

For example, the dogged persistence of a plant that goes on growing at the same slow rate despite everything that frost, blight and your dog can throw at it might indicate that it is an Oak type. The plant next to it, which is failing but still throwing out pretty flowers as if nothing is wrong, might be Agrimony. And the third plant, which grows with great exuberance until it seems to burn itself out, could be a Vervain type.

And the way to find out if these guesses are correct? – use the remedies on the plant. If you are right, then the type remedy will indeed help. If you are wrong it will not do any harm.

Sometimes people wonder about the type remedies of the plants that are used to make the remedies. Is every oak tree an Oak type? Should Vine be given to all members of the vine family? And would Aspen help the aspen tree to stop shaking for no reason?

The answer is 'no' – you can't select remedies for one of the remedy plants on this basis. Basically every plant, just like every person or every animal, needs to be treated as an individual with an individual life history and an individual approach to life. It is true that the typical vine is strong and energetic, and will take over other less forceful plants – but the typical vine exists only in imagination, just like the typical dog or the typical football player or the typical mother-in-law. Two vine plants will not grow at exactly the same rate or respond in exactly the same way to the same problem. The vine that needs Wild Rose will still seem more energetic than some other plants in your garden, but the need for Wild Rose will become apparent when you compare it with others of its species.

Giving remedies to plants

If you are using the remedies widely in the garden, for example on a whole flower-bed, then the easiest way to do this is to add them to the watering can and so make them part of your regular watering routine. Used in this way the remedies will stay in the soil and the plant will gradually absorb them along with the water. The rule of thumb is to use about five drops of each selected individual remedy, and/or ten drops of Rescue Remedy, for every gallon of water. Water all around the plants, and if possible to the extent of the root system. If you are giving remedies to trees you should try to water everywhere sheltered by the branches, as this will be the approximate size of the root system.

If you are giving the remedies to a single plant then there is no need to use so much remedy.

Instead you can put two drops of individual remedies (four of Rescue) into whatever amount of water you are going to give to the plant.

Another way to give the remedies to plants is to add them to a water sprayer and use this to mist and freshen up leaves and flowers, or to encourage newly pricked out seedlings. For a standard hand-held sprayer you need to add a couple of drops of individual remedies, and/or four drops of Rescue Remedy.

Finally, you could make up a treatment bottle for individual plants. To do this get an empty 30 ml (one ounce) dropper bottle, and put into it two drops of each selected remedy (plus four of Rescue Remedy if you are using that as well). Top this up with still mineral water and keep it in the fridge.

To give the treatment bottle mix to a plant, add four drops to your sprayer and spray the plant and the soil around it. If you need more than one sprayer-full to complete the job, add further drops to each sprayer of water. For pot plants you can add the four drops to a spoonful of water and tip this onto the plant. This is a good method to use if the plant has a visible problem that you want to address, such as mould or physical damage, since the remedy can be applied directly to the affected area.

For best results from a treatment bottle you need to repeat the dose regularly, four or more times every day until an improvement is seen.

Treating plant people

People who regularly give the remedies to animals have noticed time and time again that the state of mind of the animal's owner is often central to the state of mind of the animal. This is because many of a house animal's problems often start with the owner, and there is little point treating the animal if the out-of-balance owner is not approached at the same time and on the same level.

The same insight may well apply to plants as well. When treating houseplants, for example, it can be a good idea to look at the states of minds of the people living in the house. At the very least the person who usually looks after the plant can be assessed for likely remedies.

There is some science to back up this approach. In particular the US researcher Marcel Vogel has found that the emotions felt by a person who is tuned into a plant can have a powerful effect on the emotions that seem to be felt by the plant. In *The Secret Life of Plants* he is reported as concluding that "a Life Force, or Cosmic Energy, surrounding all living things is sharable among plants, animals and humans."

If this is so, then a positive, caring state of mind in the person looking after the plant may well influence that plant for the good. This could be the origin of the 'green fingers' phenomenon. And by the same token a negative state of mind in a plant's main carer may have a negative impact on the emotional state of the plant – and hence on its physical health. This would be the state referred to as 'having brown fingers'...

Before looking at the plant, then, it can be a good idea to look at the person taking care of the plant. The same remedy (and for the same reasons) may benefit them both.

PART 3:

Case Studies

Evidence now supports the vision of the poet and the philosopher that plants are living, breathing, communicating creatures, endowed with personality and attributes of soul. It is only we, in our blindness, who have insisted on considering them automata.

PETER TOMPKINS AND
CHRISTOPHER BIRD

About the case studies

So far we have dealt with the theory behind using the remedies to help plants. Now – how does it work in practice?

In this section I have included a number of case studies, some of them sent in by members of the public and registered Bach practitioners, others reprinted from past editions of the Bach Centre's *Newsletter*. Many of them feature the 'traditional' approach of giving Rescue Remedy, or Rescue Remedy-plus-Crab Apple, or Rescue Remedy-plus-Walnut. Others are more adventurous, and show people trying to go further and identify real 'states of mind' in the plants and apply the exact remedies needed. Results are not achieved in every case, and sometimes (especially with the older case studies) we have to try to guess for ourselves the reasoning behind the selections made. Nevertheless, I feel there is something to be learned even from people's occasional failures – and certainly much to be admired in their willingness to experiment.

As stated in the Acknowledgements, my thanks go to all the people whose stories are featured here. In many ways these reports are the most important part of this book. I hope that they will inspire you to try the remedies in your own garden.

A PLUM TREE

I used Crab Apple and Walnut on a plum tree; it had borne no fruit this year. After ten days there is a marked improvement – the tree looks healthier and the leaves are definitely uncurling.

I have found this experiment most intriguing as I cannot quite reconcile in my own mind how the remedies can possibly apply to plants.

From *The Bach Remedy Newsletter*, March 1951

THREE KINGDOMS

In the last Newsletter of March 1951, an account appears of the successful treatment of a plum tree, which ends with the remark: "I cannot quite reconcile in my own mind how the remedies can possibly apply to plants." This opens up a fascinating subject for study and conjecture. Three recent patients of mine, a tree, a butterfly and a man, show the efficacy of the Remedies in all three kingdoms.

The fractured persimmon tree

Early in November last year, a young persimmon tree was blown down by the wind and completely severed about one foot above the ground. Only one thin thread of bark joined the two sections, and as we had been absent from home when the accident occurred it was not discovered immediately.

With small hope of healing so grave an injury we placed the tree in an upright position, dressed the wound with bandages soaked in a solution of Rescue Remedy, and strapped the whole tightly between wooden splints.

I kept the dressings moist with the medicine for several days, also watering the roots freely with a weak solution. Now, after this long severe winter, our little tree is budding normally and shows no signs at all of the injury.

The premature butterfly
In the middle of March while the weather was still very cold we discovered a small copper butterfly obviously just free from her chrysalis. We took her indoors, and for a whole week she slept on a vase of flowers.

Several times each day I sat her on a drop of Rescue Remedy on my finger, thinking that perhaps the vibrations might help to revive her. At last she unfurled her proboscis and took a long draught from the drop.

The result was immediate and almost startling.

From being almost lifeless she fluttered strongly about the room, but as the weather was still cold we kept her indoors for two more days, feeding her on fresh hyacinths and Rescue Remedy. At the end of that time, one sunny morning, we opened the window and watched her fly on strong wings to freedom.

Case of acute thrombosis

Herr X of Berlin was in hospital with acute thrombosis; both legs were in plaster, and the doctors thought so seriously of his condition that his sister was summoned from Switzerland. She took with her a bottle of certain remedies, prescribed from a description of her brother's character, given to me by a mutual friend.

An immediate improvement was felt after the first few doses; the patient himself was full of renewed hope and confidence in the remedies.

As soon as the plaster could be removed, applications of these remedies with cold bandages were found to give further relief, and now after three months' treatment Herr X is able to walk a little each day in his garden and his sister can return to her home in Switzerland. Herr X was given Rock Rose, Agrimony, Holly and Impatiens. The 'wonder-drops', he calls them.

All three sufferers had experienced shock: the tree by its sudden severance from its roots; the butterfly by transition from the warm unconscious condition of the chrysalis to a cold, unaccustomed atmosphere; and the man by the sudden onslaught of a severe and painful malady.

They were probably all three suffering from pain, fear and semi-paralysis in their varying degrees.

Thirdly, all three faced imminent dissolution, whether consciously or not. And the instinct of self-preservation was in each.

Therefore, ordinary common sense first aid and treatment plus the Bach Remedies were equally necessary for them all, with the encouraging results described.

Elwin Hughes, from *The Bach Remedy Newsletter*, June 1951

A PINE TREE

A pine tree, struck by lightning, developed a black streak all down its trunk, and the needles on the branches of one side of the tree turned brown and died off. Rescue Remedy, Pine and Oak were given.

The remedies were added to buckets of water

and the trunk and roots bathed with them at frequent intervals.

The black streak disappeared in about a month, new little green needles took the place of the brown ones, and when I saw it last the tree was almost completely restored.

E. Neale, from *The Bach Remedy Newsletter*, September 1951

HAWTHORN

A privet, growing where an electric main passes under the hedge, died, and a hawthorn bush was transplanted to take its place. Not knowing that it was going to be uprooted, the gardener had pruned it only the week before; in addition it was an unsuitable season for transplantation. The hawthorn wilted, the leaves beginning to shrivel and turn brown.

I turned to Bach and selected the following remedies: Gorse (great hopelessness, depression); Clematis (unconsciousness, the wish to die); Star of Bethlehem (shock); Wild Rose (insufficient interest, resignation); Honeysuckle (living in the past).

A couple of drops of each went into the watering can filled with rainwater, and the whole bush and the surrounding soil was well sprinkled with the mixture; the following morning it looked less dejected and the un-withered leaves were crisp and green. It shed the remainder of its leaves later than the neighbouring hawthorn and now, some eight months later, it is a flourishing sturdy bush.

J. Blyth-Praeger, from *The Bach Remedy Newsletter*, December 1952

MUSK ROSE

A very backward late-planted musk rose that I watered with Olive, Clematis and Gorse is now doing well and showing flower-buds.

M. Haslehurst, from *The Bach Remedy Newsletter*, March 1954

CYCLAMEN

Six weeks ago we noticed the two blooms of our cyclamen plant were drooping and the leaves soft and weak. It was watered with the Rescue Remedy and within two minutes the blooms began to move upwards. In half an hour they were upright and in perfect health. The plant now has five blooms; the first two have only just faded. It was almost uncanny to see the stems moving upwards after the dose.

J. Silver, from *The Bach Remedy Newsletter*, March 1954

GREEN FLY

The plum trees this year were covered with green fly, so thick that you could not see the colour of trunk, branches or leaves. I sprayed with soft soap three times, but it had little effect because of the rain. Then I sprayed them with Rock Rose, Mimulus and Crab Apple. The blight disappeared and new shoots appeared where before there was nothing but black curled-up leaves.

M. Chick, from *The Bach Remedy Newsletter*,
March 1955

A PEACH TREE, AND CUT FLOWERS

A small peach tree grown from a stone was for some reason losing all its leaves in mid-summer. They withered and then fell off. I gave the tree Agrimony for I felt it was being tortured by something and Crab Apple to remove whatever it was that was harming it. I watered the ground round its roots, and sprayed the whole tree. To my surprise within a week the old leaves stopped falling, and not long after that a whole new set of fresh green leaves appeared.

I often add a drop or two of Rescue Remedy to the water in my flower vases and find the flowers keep fresh for very much longer. Also a pot plant which seemed to be dying completely recovered after I had watered it with water containing the Rescue Remedy.

N. G., from *The Bach Remedy Newsletter*, December 1956

FUCHSIA

I want to tell you about the complete resuscitation of a dying fuchsia plant which was re-potted with dire results. The poor thing was drooping in every leaf in spite of being watered in and made as comfortable as possible. We soaked it again and added several drops of the Rescue Remedy and it is now blooming and has put out several new buds.

J. C. Williams, from *The Bach Remedy Newsletter*, June 1958

PRIZE APPLES

I am sure you will be interested to hear that I won second prize at the horticultural show with apples from the little tree which, in 1953, an expert told me would never do any more good and would be dead in five years. The tree is flourishing. The first remedies I gave were Rock Rose and Aspen; next, Vervain, Chestnut Bud and Hornbeam.

K. C. P., from *The Bach Remedy Newsletter*, June 1958

ARBUTUS

An arbutus which was apparently dying was treated with the Rescue Remedy. Almost all the existing wood died, but it sprouted well from the base, making a number of foot-long shoots as well as short ones. It is now looking extremely well.

A. K. Gordon, from *The Bach Remedy Newsletter*, June 1958

GARDEN PRODUCE

I was very impressed by the effect of the Rescue Remedy on some garden produce – lettuces, mint and parsley – which I brought with me on a long train journey this weekend. I left the roots in water overnight with a few drops of the remedy added and they had quite recovered the next morning, which is not normally my experience with such things brought so far and in bad condition.

P. B., from *The Bach Remedy Newsletter*, December 1958

QUINCE

I have three times sprayed and watered a quince tree which has apparently been dying for the past two years. Some leaves are appearing on one of the 'dead' branches, and there will be fruit on the tree this year where there was none last. I used Clematis and Rock Rose.

> J. R., from *The Bach Remedy Newsletter*,
> December 1958

PEPPERS AND TOMATOES

I had to be away from home unexpectedly for five days and on my return I found my pepper plants and tomato plants (just ready to transplant) were drooping over the sides of the flats, the peppers like wet noodles that had dried.

I applied the Rescue Remedy. Very soon afterwards practically all were standing almost erect. We could see them move. Three pepper plants seemed dead, but I have kept them moistened with the Rescue Remedy, even the dried curled up leaves and stems. Two have fully recovered. The third plant has a green erect stem, even though the leaves have dried and fallen off. I am going to continue with it – perhaps it will sprout new leaves. All the other plants look as though nothing had happened.

> M. H. Berry, from *The Bach Remedy Newsletter*,
> September 1959

ANEMONES

We had a very good result with some anemones which I bought some few weeks ago. Within two or three days they looked as though they had had it: heads drooping and limp, very woebegone, and I thought they were at the point of death.

We gave them Rescue Remedy and Hornbeam because they looked as though they just could not face the future, and Agrimony because they are normally so jolly and bright. Within three hours their stems had stiffened and they were merry and bright.

E. Livingston, from *The Bach Remedy Newsletter*, December 1959

ALMOND TREE

Our almond tree has completely recovered after suffering for years from a blight which reddened and shrivelled its leaves, although the fruit remained unimpaired. I put some Rescue Remedy in a gallon of water and gave the tree a plentiful watering. I cannot say exactly how long, but it was only a few weeks later I noticed the tree again, and all its leaves were green and healthy.

E. Lee, from *The Bach Remedy Newsletter*, December 1959

CYPRESS BUSH

We treated a cypress bush with the Rescue
Remedy. It was badly attacked by the frost early
this year. It was given the Rescue Remedy every
morning for about a fortnight and it really took
on a new lease of life. It is quite a healthy and
happy bush now.

A.S., from *The Bach Remedy Newsletter*, March
1963

A NECTARINE TREE

My nectarine tree, grown from a stone, grew into
a lovely straight bushy tree in seven months.
Then all at once it began to wither away. I found
our cat had gnawed the trunk about two to three
inches above ground. I watered it liberally with
Rescue Remedy and Hornbeam and guarded it
against future attack. When spring came it went
mad in growth, with three perfect laterals and
three or four fruit spurs. I will let you know more
particulars later on.

G. Biggs, from *The Bach Remedy Newsletter*,
March 1968

TRANSPLANTED BUSH

I transplanted a small bush into what I thought
was a better position, but after four days it
seemed unhappy and droopy and the leaves

looked withered. So I made up some medicine of Star of Bethlehem for the shock of being transplanted, Honeysuckle as it might have been missing its old home, and Hornbeam to give it strength. I sprayed the whole bush with a teaspoonful of the medicine in a gallon of rainwater morning and night for five days. You would be surprised to see the bush now – happy and strong and with flower buds about to burst.

P.B., from *The Bach Remedy Newsletter*, March 1968

RESCUING A CLEMATIS

I tried putting some Rescue Remedy on a new clematis my neighbour had planted, and which seemed to be stationary. In a short time it had thrown up beautiful new green foliage.

M.H., from *The Bach Remedy Newsletter*, March 1969

PLANT PATIENTS

For the first time I have just had two plant patients. One was a vine, which certainly looked more dead than alive, leaves shrivelled with brown spots over them and altogether very sorry for itself. I told the owner to strip off its dead leaves and to water the remaining leaves, branches and roots four times a day with rain water to which was added Mimulus, Olive and Star of Bethlehem. By the following morning the improvement was really remarkable, and it then went from strength to strength, and now after ten days looks a completely healthy vine.

The other patient – a spirea – was also in a bad way and needed quite a different prescription – Crab Apple, Gorse and Cherry Plum. It also responded at once.

H.D., from *The Bach Remedy Newsletter*, March 1970

OAK FOR AN APPLE TREE

In my garden there was an apple tree in poor condition and very badly placed. I struggled for two years without success using conventional methods, except that I do not use chemicals which would harm bees or birds, but the tree continued to get every blight and disease going. I tried spasmodically with the Bach Remedies, but this year I concentrated entirely on them and nothing else: Crab Apple to cleanse, Agrimony as the tree was tortured, Oak as it struggled for survival. Now we have a bumper crop and not a single apple dropped. Many people have commented on it.

P. M. Briers, from *The Bach Remedy Newsletter*, September 1970

AMERICAN BLIGHT

Here at Mount Vernon ... we had an old apple tree which was covered with American blight one summer. We sprayed the trunk and the branches with Crab Apple and Agrimony, for we felt that the old tree disliked being unclean and felt tortured. We continued to spray for one week, and watered the root area at the same time. The blight soon disappeared, and the tree has never suffered from it again.

Nora Weeks (quoted by Philip Chancellor) in *Illustrated Handbook of the Bach Flower Remedies)*

A DAMAGED TRUNK

We applied Rescue Remedy Cream to a sapling's damaged trunk and it healed beautifully.

John Ramsell, in *Questions & Answers*

RHODODENDRONS

You will be interested to hear of the success of the Rescue Remedy on one of my favourite miniature Rhododendrons. It succumbed to the drought when we were on holiday. It was completely leafless and brittle and appeared a hopeless case.

I applied the Rescue Remedy liquid to one half of the bush which was 12 inches in diameter and 6 inches high. The treated section is now covered in glossy green leaves and dormant flower buds, whilst the untreated section is completely dead. This plant is eighteen years old and has been transplanted at least six times as I always try to take my plants with me when we move. I shall never cease to be grateful for having been introduced to Dr. Bach's remedies.

S. D. Morgan, from *The Bach Remedy Newsletter*, March 1974

PASSION FRUIT VINE

Mrs K. Barry of Inglewood is a very keen gardener, and besides helping others with the remedies she also treats her plants. She tells us of her passion fruit vine, which has looked miserable for a few years, but this spring she gave it several doses of Crab Apple and Star of Bethlehem, throwing jug-fuls over the whole plant, and now, "I have had beautiful fruit".

From *The Bach Remedy Newsletter*, September 1974

TOMATO SEEDLINGS

The last time I transplanted tomato seedlings I gave each plant a dose of the Rescue Remedy. The plants stood upright from the time of transplanting and these particular plants yielded heavier fruit than any we have grown here.

A. N. Small, from *The Bach Remedy Newsletter*, December 1974

MOVING HOUSE, AND A POINSETTIA

All the plants and trees which we had to move to our new home during long, dry and hot spells last summer did settle down and are growing nicely now. We moved roses, and rooted cuttings, fuchsias, hollies and a lilac tree, and many other plants and shrubs. They all had Rescue sprayed over them each day and were watered with them as well and were quite happy. Some found it a bit difficult but soon settled down.

Then we had a poinsettia given to us which had been very badly treated and had lost all its leaves but three. We gave it Rescue and put a little on our fingers, gently rubbing it on the leaves and all over the stems once a day. After a week we used Olive every other day and carried on for over one month. The remaining leaves did not drop off and the plant began to have new shoots and new leaves. It is now a big, beautiful and strong plant, and it was amazing to watch the transformation.

F. O. Gutzmer, from *The Bach Remedy Newsletter*, December 1974

AFRICAN VIOLET NUMBER 1

I had an African violet given to me and only a few days later I carelessly dropped it on its head when dusting. It stopped drinking and all the flowers fell off and the leaves appeared limp.

I gave it the Rescue Remedy three times a day for two days, then twice a week. After about a month it had quite revived and is now a healthy plant. I really thought it had died of shock, and I felt like a murderess!

L. Hitchins, from *The Bach Remedy Newsletter*, March 1975

AFRICAN VIOLET NUMBER 2

I have had good results with indoor African violets. I frequently take leaf cuttings and find the following method works well:

Put the leaf cutting (with about 2.5 to 3 centimetres of stem) into an egg cup and fill with enough tepid water to cover the stem but not the leaf. Add a few drops of ready-prepared Rescue

Remedy and Walnut and change the water every two or three days.

The remedies need to be used for about a week or so, and then you can switch to plain water. Keep the cuttings on a light window sill, but not in very hot sunshine; they should root in a few weeks.

I use this method throughout the year, as sometimes the leaves accidentally break off as I water the plants, and it is much less messy than garden compost.

Hilary Leigh in correspondence with the author.

MORE TOMATO SEEDLINGS

Having planted out my outdoor tomato seedlings I had three surplus, which were poor specimens. They were thrown on top of the compost heap. In three days' time I noticed a gap in one row and having no more plants I recollected the three thrown-out plants which were by now almost completely withered. These were watered in with Rescue Remedy and sprayed for the next two days.

In three days they were beginning to grow and in a month it was obvious that they were the most healthy, the most disease-free and the largest of all my twenty plants. They yielded the best trusses, and although they had to be gathered

green due to bad autumn weather, they all
ripened well inside and were of excellent flavour.

T. W. Hyne Jones, from *The Bach Remedy
Newsletter*, March 1975

PEACH TREES AND CHRISTMAS ROSES

Crab Apple has effected a complete cure for two
peach trees growing against an old brick wall.
They had peach-leaf curl very badly. It has also
done the same for a disease common to Christmas
roses, black spot on the leaves which spreads
until the leaf rots.

M. Rolph, from *The Bach Remedy Newsletter*,
April 1975

MILDEWED GRAPES

Last week we found that the bunches of grapes
on the grape vine in our greenhouse were
showing signs of mildew. We sprayed them with
clear water and a few drops of Crab Apple. All
the grapes now appear to be clean.

J. and H. B., from T*he Bach Remedy Newsletter*,
December 1975

PLANTING

I always water the seeds of flowers and vegetables
when put in the ground with a solution of Star of

Bethlehem and Hornbeam to allay any shock of planting and give them the strength to grow. It is astonishing how they respond.

W. G., from *The Bach Remedy Newsletter*,
December 1975

A WINDOW BOX

I have four geranium plants in one window-sill box and four in the other. In early June when they were in flower we had terribly high winds and I thought I would lose them. They were all bent over.

I brought them in and replanted them and firmed them in well, and gave them Rescue Remedy. Later I gave them more, and not a leaf dropped, as though nothing had happened, and they all bloomed magnificently.

M. C., from *The Bach Remedy Newsletter*,
December 1975

BLACK SPOT

I have a bed of Prima Ballerina roses and each year they are troubled with black spot. The black spot remedy from the garden centre is never very satisfactory as it causes the leaves to dry up and drop off, leaving a very sad-looking plant.

This year I have put eight drops of Crab Apple

and ten drops of Rescue Remedy into a can of water. I make sure it goes on the leaves as well as giving the roots a good drink. I have done this about once a month so far and I am delighted with the result. My roses are very healthy with hardly any sign of black spot – just the odd leaf which can easily be removed. What is more they have flowered continuously this year with many more buds to follow.

'A lady in Staffordshire', from *The Bach Remedy Newsletter*, April 1990

IN THE KITCHEN

We run a small restaurant. When we buy the parsley from the supermarket it is more dead than alive, but a spray and a drink of Rescue Remedy and all is well and in good shape. This treatment works wonders for limp lettuces too! A soak in Rescue Remedy water and they are unbelievably crisp.

'M.H., Portugal', from *The Bach Remedy Newsletter*, December 1990

HYACINTH BULBS

When our cat was ill his water bowl contained the remedies we prescribed for him. I used to empty the bowl daily on the same piece of soil in the garden. The year previously, I had planted some cheap Hyacinth bulbs there. When the bulbs came up this year, much to our surprise, all of the bulbs had divided, and instead of three rigid blooms we had a carpet of first quality blooms that were truly beautiful. The bulbs on either side of the path, which had not received the remedies, remained single blooms.

Since that time whenever I rinse the bottles that contained remedies, I always pour them on the bulbs alongside the path. Now, they are just coming through, lots of them, and all of them are divided.

Quoted in Philip Chancellor, *Illustrated Handbook of the Bach Flower Remedies*

BROKEN STEMS

I have successfully used Rescue Remedy drops for plants experiencing trauma. Once my niece dropped the plant she was planting and it broke in a few places, so we taped the stems, planted it and gave it some Rescue Remedy. Occasionally when transplanting I give plants Rescue Remedy if they appear traumatised.

Laura Tilley in correspondence with the author.

ALOE VERA

I decided to try a Bach Flower Remedy for my aloe vera plant. I have had this plant for about four years and it never did particularly well. Other aloes I have had in the past flourished. This one moved with me a few times so had experienced a variety of windows and environments, but did not do better or worse in any. It was always rather languid. Its spines would often droop and it only had a few new growths.

I asked a friend what he thought and he felt that the aloe missed its family and its mother. He suggested getting another aloe plant as a friend to the first plant, and putting the first plant outside now and then.

I did this and it helped ... but it was when I mixed up some Honeysuckle (laying the past to rest) and began administering it that it really perked up. I have even started taking the tincture myself – my mother died when I was nine, so I could understand how the plant felt.

I have been doing this for about four or five weeks now and the spines are straight and strong, with new growth evident. I administer the mix about two to three times a day (because I am at work most of the day) in the direct centre of the aloe. Often I will hold one spine while I take the remedy myself, and commune with the aloe plant, letting it know that I too lost my mother and that we are laying the past to rest, not forgetting.

Laura Tilley in correspondence with the author.

RESCUE REMEDY

I have had very good experiences for many years using Rescue Remedy in the garden when I move, divide or put in new plants. I also use Rescue Remedy when I'm re-potting or moving my plants inside the house, watering with this for about a week. When I buy new plants I use water with Rescue Remedy at once, since the change of surroundings and atmosphere especially in winter must be very rough for the plant: out from the greenhouse, outside in the cold and then inside again, often in a drier atmosphere than in the greenhouse.

I often buy plants that the gardener has put on sale, since they are drooping or looking bad. Although I like plants and have many of them, I don't consider myself to have especially green fingers, but I nearly always keep the cheap plants alive (and put them in the garden in spring...)

Lately I have experimented with a mix of Rescue Remedy and Crab Apple against parasites like mites and mould. I use Rescue Remedy because the plant actually is under attack and must be stressed – and the Crab Apple is to help the cleansing process. I water and sprinkle the plants until the parasites are gone, and if the mite attack is very persistent I add a little brown soap to the water.

Although I haven't got a lot of experience using this mixture – I started last year when all my son's cacti were infected with mould – it seems to work. And it hasn't been necessary to use soap as often as before.

And last – as a curiosity – I use Rescue Remedy when I change water in my aquarium, putting in one drop to every litre of water. I still use special water preparations to clear and smoothen the water, (if I haven't got clean rainwater), but both plants and fish seem more unstressed when Rescue Remedy is used as well.

Susanne Hamilton-Clausen in correspondence with the author.

A GARDENER WRITES FROM VERMONT

In the summer months I am a gardener. I maintain and plant gardens for about a dozen clients, most of whose gardens are of the old-fashioned perennial kind, using tried and true varieties that are hardy in our cold zone three to four.

Some of the nurseries that I purchase from are in a slightly warmer zone. I have begun using Walnut, Honeysuckle and Rescue Remedy in the transplanting process, and all of my gardens seem to be healthy and happy. I do talk to my gardens and extol their beauty out loud. One could only wonder what a passer-by would think...

I also love growing herbs and vegetables from seed. I mostly sow the seeds directly into the ground, but I do start some plants. Lavender is one – the seeds take a while to germinate. One must have patience, so I use Impatiens both for myself and for the seedling during this process.

I use Crab Apple for any disease that tries to challenge the new plants. The dosage is usually a couple of drops per quart of water, sometimes a dropperful from a prepared treatment bottle to a larger container. And when plants have a problem like red spider or aphids I use Crab Apple then as well.

Isabelle Hadley in correspondence with the author.

TWO SUCCESSES AND A SECOND THOUGHT

I would like to share with you my two most successful cases. The first client was an indoor cyclamen plant that had developed yellowing leaves. It was given Crab Apple in a small watering can – four drops to a can – and was watered from the bottom, as cyclamens are supposed to be. It regained its vigour after just one day's dosage.

Then, several years ago, I transplanted and pruned in the same week a small rose bush, much against my inclination. It was given Rescue Remedy and not only did it survive this drastic upheaval, but it produced unusually abundant roses all summer long.

Not all of my experiences were so successful. I tried to coax a tree peony seedling with Larch, Rescue Remedy and Olive. It remained weak, and did not survive the winter.

In retrospect I think I should have used Elm, as the poor seedling was overwhelmed by the other plants. Another remedy it occurs to me to have tried was Walnut, for too much sensitivity to the surroundings.

Rhoma Mostel in correspondence with the author.

WALNUT

I have noticed that Walnut is an incredible help for the new plants that I buy. They do not 'get sick' as some of them used to when they were put into their new environment.

I have also noticed that Rescue Remedy enlivens them very quickly and often makes them bloom instantaneously. This is what happened with my Gardenia – I have just bought it and several new flowers appeared in two days.

Igor Pietkiewicz in correspondence with the author.

A TROPICAL PLANT

We had to transplant a large-leaf tropical plant, which was about four feet tall, due to an encroaching fence. The new site had the perfect environment and soil, but the plant was very unhappy. We watched leaf by large leaf turn yellow and die over a course of two or three weeks. I would cut them off, talk to the plant, all to no avail.

I remembered Rescue Remedy (I am usually a 'people' practitioner) and knew I had to try. I did not have a sprayer bottle, and wasn't sure of the dosage, so I brought our family treatment bottle to the plant and dropped the remedy directly into the middle of it, and all over its one remaining leaf.

After two days of dosing the plant around three times a day I realised that its one leaf was not going to turn yellow and die. After five or six days I noticed new growth. After about one and a half weeks the new growth was healthy and strong – by this time I was only dosing it once a day.

Today the plant is back on its feet and thriving, with what is oddly enough a darker more vibrant colour than before.

Debbie Weatherby in correspondence with the author.

ORANGES AND LEMONS

My mother has an orange and a lemon tree in her garden. A few years ago they were attacked by plant lice. Both trees were covered, and began to fade badly.

We didn't want to use chemicals on the trees because we like to eat their fruit, so I tried using Bach Flower Remedies on them. I chose Rescue Remedy, plus Crab Apple and Centaury – I felt that the trees needed help to stand up to the lice. For about four days I sprayed both trees with the remedies, and watered them in as well. But when there was no immediate effect I stopped using them.

Ten days later I visited my mother and was amazed to see that most of the lice were gone; I thought my mother must have used some other treatment on the trees, but she hadn't. It must have been the remedies working, because normally these lice are very difficult to get rid of. So I sprayed the trees again with the same remedies, and next day they were free of the infestation.

Giusi Moretta in correspondence with the author.

TWO STORIES

A *Coleus*, which I am keeping as a houseplant, became rather top-heavy due to my ignorance about nipping the tops off. One of the stems broke, although it did not come off completely.

I sprayed it with a simple solution of Rescue Remedy, Crab Apple and Walnut, and rested the broken stem on the ivy next to it. When I looked again, maybe a week later, to my amazement the stem had glued itself back on. It can once again hold its own weight, and shows its scar and the bonding material around it, just like glue.

I also have a *Ficus Benjamina Starlight* whose

leaves were falling rather a lot. I sprayed it with the same mix I gave to the *Coleus*, adding Gentian because I felt it was probably despondent. (If it had been wilting I would have used Gorse.)

After the first spraying it only lost three leaves. On the second spraying three leaves fell again – and the leaf fall definitely lessened over the first week.

One evening I noticed that the plant had actually become greener. Small new shoots and leaves had started to grow on the ends from which the leaves had fallen.

I changed the position of the plant, placing it above a radiator as I thought it had been too cold where it was, and with the remedies and the extra heat it is now doing well. All in all the treatment took about a month.

Ester Naylor, in correspondence with the author.

PART 4:

Reference Section

It is need and interest above all that induce the growth of our abilities; a motivated observer develops faculties that a casual spectator may never be aware of.

EVELYN FOX KELLER

Some typical situations

There are a number of problems that any gardener will confront time and time again. What follows is an alphabetical list of some of these common situations, with some suggestions to get you thinking. Remember that these are not combinations that will always apply, but simply lists of remedies that may prove useful in these circumstances. (And Rescue Remedy is taken as read as the emergency remedy for all these occasions.)

DEHYDRATION
- Oak to support the struggle
- Olive to give energy
- Rock Rose or Mimulus for fear of death
- Wild Rose for resignation
- Willow for self-pity

FAILURE TO THRIVE
- Centaury for plants whose vitality has been sapped by the growth of other more rampant plants
- Clematis to bring the plant into the present
- Gentian to give encouragement
- Gorse to give hope and the will to live

- Hornbeam to get the plant started
- Larch to give self-belief
- Mustard where there is no apparent reason
- Water Violet for plants forced to grow too near others
- Wild Oat to give a sense of purpose
- Wild Rose to remove apathy

FLOWERS AND FRUIT, LACK OF

- Centaury to allow the plant to stand up to pests etc.
- Crab Apple to promote self-acceptance by the plant
- Gentian to give encouragement
- Hornbeam to provide the energy needed to get started
- Impatiens to give patience and allow slow growth (you could take this yourself as well)
- Olive if the plant is exhausted after years of flowering or fruiting
- Rock Water for self-contained, repressed plants

FROST

- Elm to help the plant to cope with the added pressure
- Star of Bethlehem for shock
- Sweet Chestnut for anguish

OVER-WATERING
- Gentian for the setback
- Olive to give the strength to resist
- Vervain for yourself, so that you can restrain your watering in future...

PESTS, FUNGUS, ROT ETC.
- Agrimony for feelings of torture
- Centaury to help stand up to the infestation
- Crab Apple as a cleanser
- Star of Bethlehem for the shock

PHYSICAL DAMAGE
- Rescue Cream as a salve
- Star of Bethlehem for shock

TRANSPLANTING
- Honeysuckle to help the plant let go of the past
- Star of Bethlehem for shock
- Walnut for change
- Try watering the remedies into the new hole where the plant is to go before you put the plant in

WILTING LEAVES
- Gentian to give encouragement
- Gorse to give hope
- Hornbeam or Olive to give energy
- Willow for self-pity

Further reading

DR BACH AND HIS WORK

There are many hundreds of books on the remedies and their use. Some are more reliable than others; some are downright unreliable. The books I have listed here are all written by people who have been associated with the Bach Centre at one time or another, and as such they can be relied on to follow the original, simple methods that Dr Bach himself advocated.

- *The Twelve Healers and Other Remedies* by Dr Edward Bach.
- *Bach Flower Remedies Step by Step* by Judy Howard.
- *The Bach Remedies Workbook* by Stefan Ball.
- *Questions and Answers* by John Ramsell.
- *Illustrated Handbook of the Bach Flower Remedies* by Phillip Chancellor.
- *Bach Flower Remedies for Women* by Judy Howard.
- *Bach Flower Remedies for Men* by Stefan Ball.
- *Growing Up with Bach Flower Remedies* by Judy Howard.
- *Bach Flower Remedies for Animals* by Stefan Ball and Judy Howard.
- *Heal Thyself* by Dr Edward Bach.

- *The Original Writings of Edward Bach* edited by John Ramsell and Judy Howard.
- *The Medical Discoveries of Edward Bach, Physician* by Nora Weeks.
- *The Story of Mount Vernon* by Judy Howard.

In addition there is a cassette called *Getting to Know the Bach Flower Remedies* and two videos, *Bach Flower Remedies: A Further Understanding*, and *The Light That Never Goes Out*. These, plus all the above books, are available from the Dr Edward Bach Centre (for the address see below).

PLANTS AND EMOTIONS
The following books were useful in helping to shed a little light on this aspect of plant life:
- *A Feeling for the Organism: The Life and Work of Barbara McClintock* by Evelyn Fox Keller (W. H. Freeman & Co, 1983).
- *The Biophilia Hypothesis* edited by Stephen Kellert and Edward Wilson (Island Press, 1993).
- *The Secret Life of Plants* by Peter Tompkins and Christopher Bird (Harper & Row, 1973).

Useful addresses

Information on the remedies and their use, and referral to registered practitioners and training opportunities in the UK and throughout the world:

THE DR EDWARD BACH CENTRE
(incorporating The Dr Edward Bach Foundation and the Dr Edward Bach Healing Trust)
Mount Vernon
Bakers Lane
Sotwell
Oxon
OX10 0PZ
United Kingdom
Tel: 01491 834678
Fax: 01491 825022
Email: bach@bachcentre.com
Website: http://www.bachcentre.com

Sales of Bach Flower Remedies in the UK and information on local availability throughout the world:

BACH FLOWER REMEDIES LTD
A. Nelson & Co Ltd
Broadheath House
83 Parkside
London, SW19 5LP
United Kingdom
Tel: 0181 780 4200
Fax: 0181 780 5871

USA
All sales and educational information for the USA:
Nelson Bach USA Ltd
100 Research Drive
Wilmington
MA 01887
USA
Tel: (Sales)   1 508 988 3833
Tel: (Education)   1 800 334 0843

AUSTRALIA
Martin & Pleasance
PO Box 2054
Richmond
3121 Victoria
Australia
Tel: 3 942 77422
Fax: 3 942 88431

SOUTH AFRICA
Vital Health Foods
PO Box 191
Production Street
7580 Kuilscriver
Tel: 2 190 33151
Fax   2 190 33158

Index
References to Remedies are in bold.

A
African violet 73
Agrimony 19, 47, 93
almond tree 66
aloe vera 79–80
anemones 66
anguish 25
animals 2
anxiety 24
apathy 26
apple trees 63, 69, 70
arbutus 64
Aspen 19

B
Bach, Dr Edward 11–17
Bach Flower Remedies 1–4,
    45–8
    and animals 2
    cultivation of 28–30
    discovery of 15–17, 34–5
    efficacy of 29, 40–2
    and emotions 18–27
    selection of 42–5
Beech 19
bitterness 27
black spot 75, 76–7
blight 66, 69, 70
boredom 26
butterflies 57–8

C
calmness 25, 26
case studies, introduction 55–6
Centaury 19, 91, 92, **93**

Cerato 20
change, unsettled by 25
Cherry Plum 20
Chestnut Bud 20
Chicory 20
cleansing 21
Clematis 20, 91
clematis, case study 68
coleus 86
confidence 19, 22, 24, 25
contamination 21
control 25
courage 23, 24
Crab Apple 21, 92, 93
cuttings 73–4
cyclamen 61, 83
cypress 67

D
decisiveness 24
dehydration 91
despair 21, 25
despondency 21, 26
discouragement 21
diseases of new plants 82 *and
    see* black spot, blight,
    fungus, leaves curling,
    mildew, mould, rot *see also*
    pests
domination 25
dosages 48–50
dreaminess 20
drifting 26
dropped plants 73, 78
drought 70–1